'Domestic Bliss'

RAVETTE BOOKS

This edition first published by
Ravette Books Limited 1990

Printed and bound for Ravette Books Limited,
3 Glenside Estate, Star Road,
Partridge Green, Horsham,
West Sussex RH13 8RA
by B L & U Printing, Wellingborough

ISBN: 1 85304 322 2

Garfield

'Domestic Bliss'

In this energy hungry World, Garfield believes in conserving his own unnatural resources.

He's hard pressed to do any ironing; he throws in the towel at washing; he can't be sucked into vacuuming, he messes up any attempt at cleaning and he makes a meal out of any cooking.

When it comes to domestic duties, Garfield creates his own environmental disaster – the 'Clean-House' effect!

TOO MUCH COFFEE, GARFIELD?

I MADE MY WORLD FAMOUS COFFEE THIS MORNING, GARFIELD

COME ON... IT'S NOT THAT BAD!... HAVE SOME!

OH, ALL RIGHT

BUT JUST A SMALL SLICE

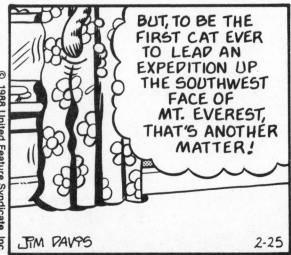

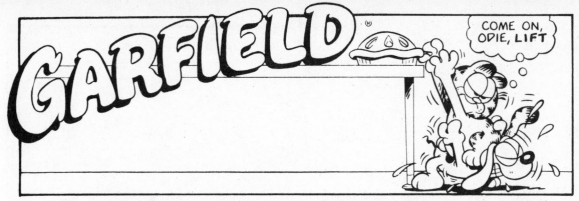

WHEN I CAN'T SLEEP, IT SEEMS LIKE EVERY SOUND IN THE HOUSE IS MAGNIFIED

THUD THUD THUD THUD THUD

MUST YOU?!

JIM DAVIS 3-30

MAYBE A GOOD BOOK WILL HELP ME SLEEP

A GOOD, BIG BOOK

JIM DAVIS

WHAP WHAP WHAP

SLEEP! SLEEP! SLEEP!

3-31

A selection of Garfield books published by Ravette

Garfield Landscapes

Garfield The All-Round Sports Star	£2.95
Garfield The Irresistible	£2.95
Garfield On Vacation	£2.95
Garfield Weighs In!	£2.95
Garfield I Hate Mondays	£2.95
Garfield Special Delivery	£2.95
Garfield Another Serve	£2.95
Garfield Wraps It Up	£2.95
Garfield This Is Your Life	£2.95
Garfield Sheer Genius	£2.95
Garfield The Incurable Romantic	£2.95
Garfield Goes Wild	£2.95
Garfield Rebel Without a Clue!	£2.95

Garfield Pocket books

No. 1 Garfield The Great Lover	£2.50
No. 2 Garfield Why Do You Hate Monday?	£2.50
No. 3 Garfield Does Pooky Need You?	£2.50
No. 4 Garfield Admit It Odie's OK!	£2.50
No. 5 Garfield Two's Company	£2.50
No. 6 Garfield What's Cooking?	£2.50
No. 7 Garfield Who's Talking?	£2.50
No. 8 Garfield Strikes Again	£2.50
No. 9 Garfield Here's Looking At You	£2.50
No. 10 Garfield We Love You Too	£2.50
No. 11 Garfield Here We Go Again	£2.50
No. 12 Garfield Life and Lasagne	£2.50
No. 13 Garfield In The Pink	£2.50
No. 14 Garfield Just Good Friends	£2.50
No. 15 Garfield Plays It Again	£2.50
No. 16 Garfield Flying High	£2.50
No. 17 Garfield On Top Of The World	£2.50
No. 18 Garfield Happy Landings	£2.50
No. 19 Garfield Going Place	£2.50
No. 20 Garfield Le Magnifique!	£2.50

Garfield TV Specials

Here Comes Garfield	£2.95
Garfield On The Town	£2.95
Garfield In The Rough	£2.95
Garfield In Disguise	£2.95
Garfield In Paradise	£2.95
Garfield Goes To Hollywood	£2.95
A Garfield Christmas	£2.95
Garfield's Thanksgiving	£2.95
The Second Garfield Treasury	£5.95
The Third Garfield Treasury	£5.95
The Fourth Garfield Treasury	£5.95
The Fifth Garfield Treasury	£5.95
Garfield A Weekend Away	£4.95
Garfield How to Party	£3.95

All these books are available at your local bookshop or newsagent, or can be ordered direct from the publisher. Just tick the titles you require and fill in the form below. Prices and availability subject to change without notice.

Ravette Books Limited, 3 Glenside Estate, Star Road, Partridge Green, Horsham, West Sussex RH13 8RA

Please send a cheque or postal order and allow the following for postage and packing. UK: Pocket books and TV Specials – 45p for one book plus 20p for the second book and 15p for each additional book. Landscape Series – 50p for one book plus 30p for each additional book. Other titles – 85p for one book plus 60p for each additional book.

Name ....

Address ....

....